A CLOUD OF SUMMER

and other new haiku

A CLOUD

OF SUMMER
and other new haiku

by Doris Johnson
Illustrated by W. T. Mars

FOLLETT PUBLISHING COMPANY

Chicago **F** *New York*

Follett Publishing Company
1010 West Washington Boulevard
Chicago, Illinois 60607

Library of Congress Catalog Card Number: AC67-10691

First Printing

T/L 1434

because of Lyn

A cloud of summer
tumbled into bowl—fluffy
rice for me to eat!

Please to blow, wind, blow!
Bow the trees! Scatter the clouds!
Set my kite dancing!

8

Peace, red dragonfly.
May I touch your fairy wing—
softly? O! Come back!

What? Sir Bumble Bee,
would you think to sting me? Go!
Sting the sweet clover!

Behind apricot—
bamboo. Behind bamboo—pine.
O happy garden.

Count the stepping stones
to your garden-place of peace
and soon return home.

13

Paper lantern lights,
 trembling wind bell, scent of rose.
 O summer evening!

14

I am a flower
name of Hana. See me nod
like blossom in rain.

16

The spider web gleams,
   a silken, dew-jeweled snare.
   Ah, poor dragonfly!

From the rice paddy
wafts a moonlit veil of mist
and song of cricket.

Behold, the gray mouse
   lays up his wealth grain by grain.
   Soon he will have much.

See old wrinkled sun
bobbing upon the water
like ripe persimmon.

The painted dragon
of the sea sleeps today. Do
you hear him snoring?

21

Sunshiny dewdrops
twinkle like far-distant stars
in a sky of grass.

22

August Mr. Star,
whose eye is bright with wisdom,
what is it you see?

Blue shadows gliding
  beneath ice on pond are gold
  fish awaiting spring.

Hold the polished stone.
  How warm it is from the sun!
  How cool from the sea!

He wears a snow crown,
   this Emperor of mountains,
   and rules the winter.

Morning glory vine
embroiders flower pattern
upon bamboo fence.

Rare is the incense
as mist rises from censer
of gardenia bloom.

A nightingale trills.
Dazzled plum blossoms scatter
like tissue snowflakes.

Ah see! The raindrops
splash and ripple in the pool
like ten thousand frogs.

Under the red bridge
a stream runs—splish-splash! Over
bridge I run—clik-clak!

Sleep, baby child, sleep,
  while moon shadows of plum boughs
  drowse upon your cheek.

Your song split the sky,
O sun-setting cicada.
See! The stars peep through.

Lo, the butterfly
   rests on a golden cushion
   of chrysanthemum.

A drop of dew fell
on red silk of peony
and made a pink pearl.

Garnet gems to eat
are seeds of pomegranate.
Sweet taste glows on tongue.

Honorable hat
of straw, whose shade I enjoy,
come, we run in sun.

Flaming maple leaves
in a festival of fire
tint the sky autumn.

O purple river,
  bear my lantern through shadowed
  pine woods to the sea.

Snowflakes fall to earth
 lightly as white-kitten-steps.
What sound is so still?

In a silver world
among the snow-bent bamboos
a ghost sparrow flits.

O little gold bells
hanging from the cherry branch,
sing *chira-chira*.

Icicle in sun
flashing blue fire, melts. Dripping,
dripping, crystal bells.

Lady Moon, come down!
O sit upon my pillow
and tell me a dream.

Porcelain and silk
	is Empress doll. Candles flare;
	tiny fan flutters.

See! Each soap bubble
in most honorable bath
contains a rainbow.

My treasure ship comes!
    Behold its gossamer sails
  filled with golden wind!

Silver star in cage
  is winking firefly. But star
  needs sky—thus. Farewell!